C000254078

SEVEN DEADLY SINS
START HERE

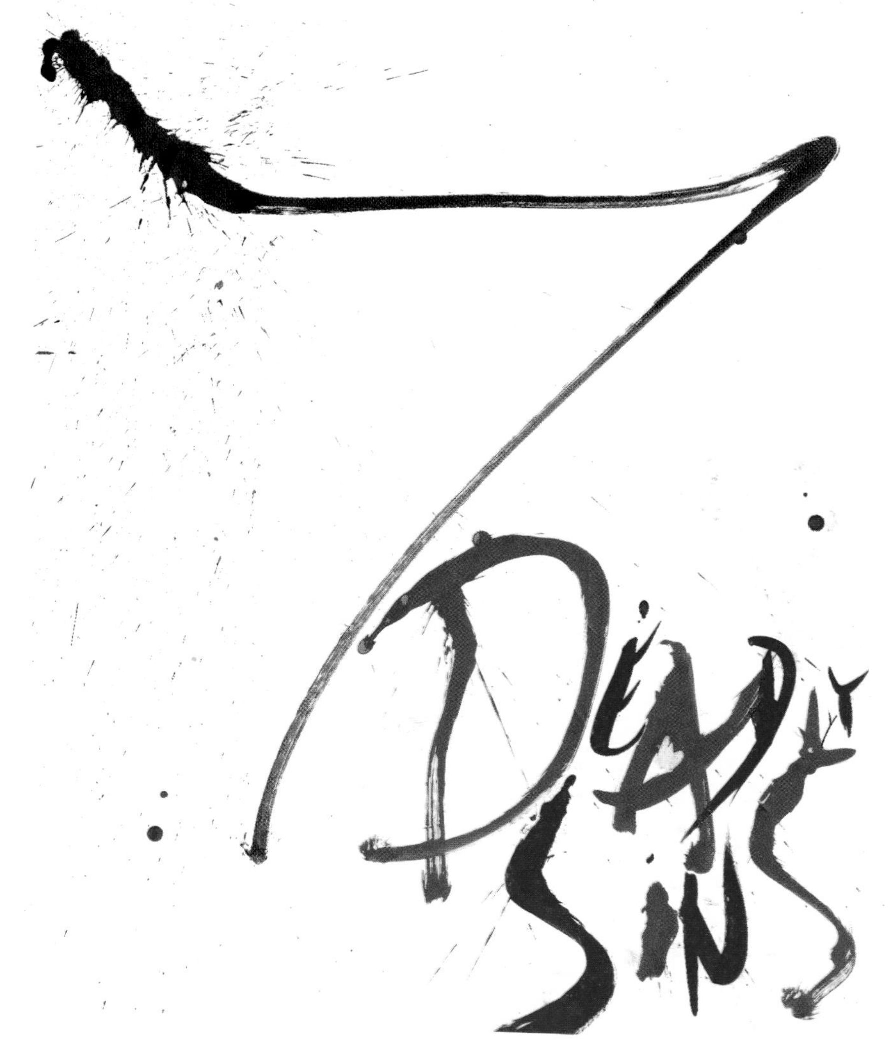
7
DEADLY
SINS

THIS BOOK IS DEDICATED
TO MY FAMILY
WITH APOLOGIES
FOR THE NAUGHTY BITS.
BUT YOU KNOW — WELL
— IT IS ABOUT SINS

Hamish Hamilton · London

HAMISH HAMILTON LTD

Penguin Books Ltd, 27 Wrights Lane, London W8 5TZ (Publishing & Editorial)
and Harmondsworth, Middlesex, England (Distribution & Warehouse)
Viking Penguin Inc., 40 West 23rd Street, New York, New York 10010, U.S.A.
Penguin Books Australia Ltd, Ringwood, Victoria, Australia
Penguin Books Canada Limited, 2801 John Street, Markham, Ontario, Canada L3R 1B4
Penguin Books (N.Z.) Ltd, 182–190 Wairau Road, Auckland 10, New Zealand

First published in Great Britain 1987
by Hamish Hamilton Ltd

British Library Cataloguing Publication Data

Scarfe, Gerald
Scarfe's seven deadly sins.
1. English wit and humor, Pictorial
I. Title
741.5′942 NC1479

ISBN 0-241-12394-1

Printed in Great Britain by
William Clowes Ltd, Beccles

BEWARE THESE LITTLE DEVILS
DON'T THINK THEY DON'T APPLY TO YOU.
SLOTH
ANGER
ENVY
GLUTTONY
AVARICE
LUST
PRIDE

Lust

LUST

LUST
BEFORE

Lust After

— That's what you get folks for making Whoopee —

LUST IN THE DAYS OF CHIVALRY

Lust
THIS SHOULD NOT BE DONE BEFORE THE ROYAL TOAST

Lust
LOVE FOR SALE
LIKE A HORRIBLE TIME DEARIE?
PROSTITUTION

IT'S WHAT THE PUBLIC WANT
THE PORNOGRAPHER

RAPE

Lust

COPULATION EQUALS POPULATION

POPULATION EXPLOSION

Lust

Are you dying for love?

GOURMETS' NIGHTMARE

TOO MUCH PORK AND APPLE SAUCE!

For The Really Ravenous
Genetic Engineering
Moo!
This one can milk itself
Gluttony

BIGGER CHOPS — BIGGER PROFITS

THE SMOKER

EMITTING FUMES FROM THIS END. ACCEPTABLE

EMITTING FUMES FROM THIS END - UNACCEPTABLE

THE DRINKER

OH COME ON — IF HE CAN'T HAVE A LITTLE DRINK AND DRIVE ONCE IN A WHILE — IT'S A DULL OLD WORLD!

DIDN'T SHPILL A DROP!

REAL MANS STUFF

Gluttony

Ooooh – I know I'm terrible
DIET CHOCOLATE CAKE
SLIMO
THE DIETER

FOOD
MOUNTAINS
KEEP OUT

Gluttony

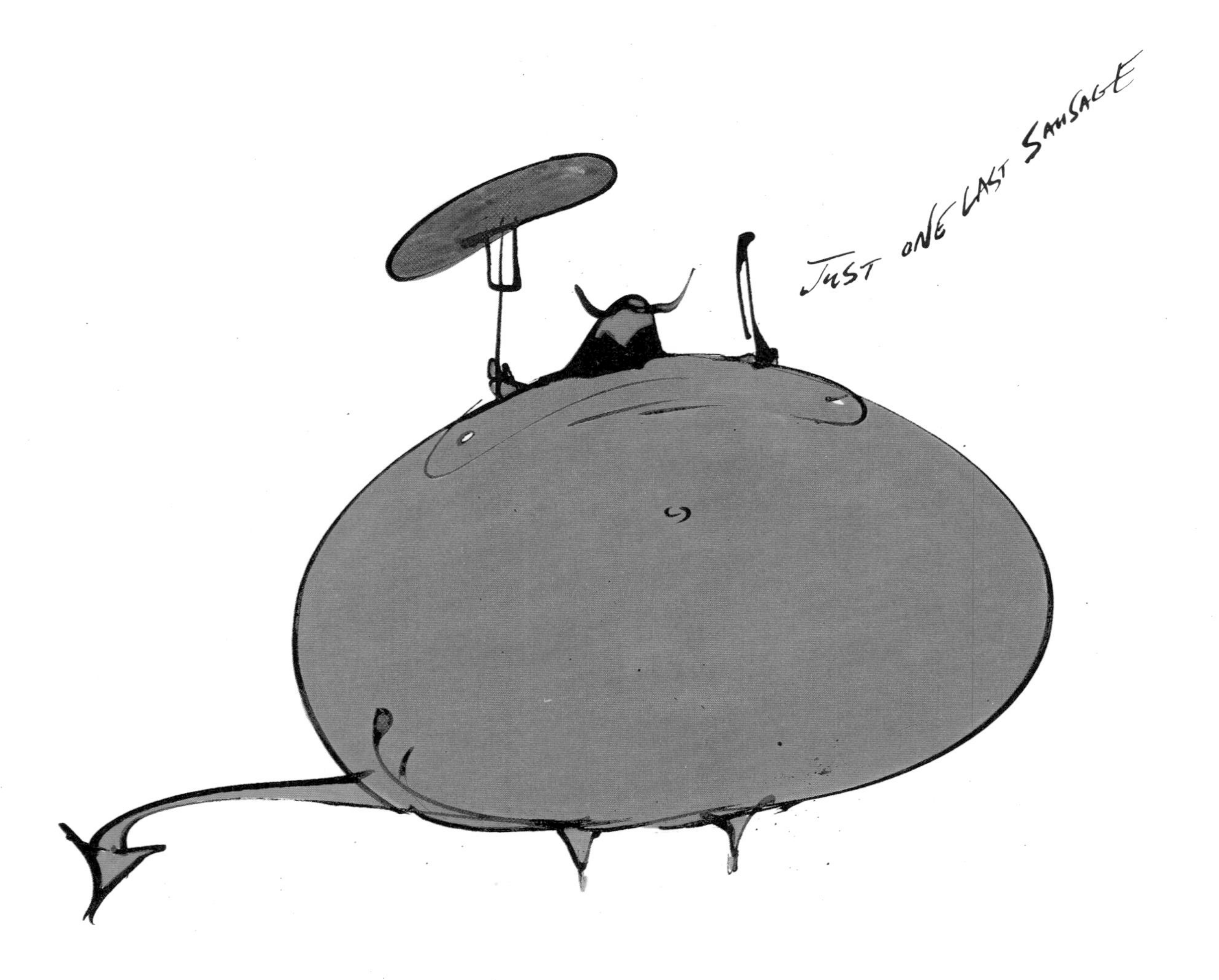
JUST ONE LAST SAUSAGE

Avarice

WHAT'S WRONG WITH BEING
A GREEDY BASTARD?

Avarice

THE GLITTERING DEVIL OF GREED

Avarice

THE ARMS SALESMEN

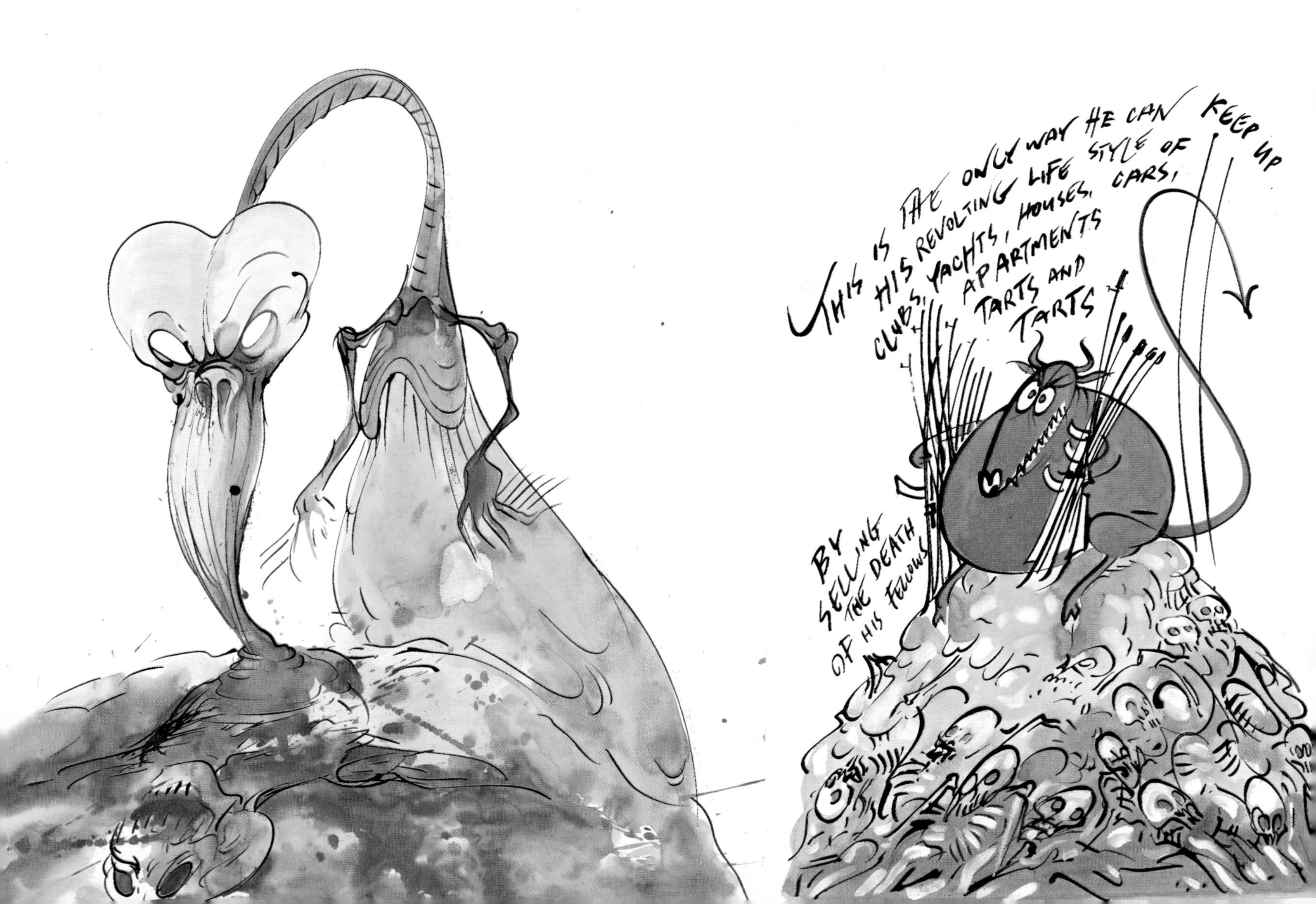

IF I DON'T DO IT, SOMEONE ELSE WILL.
DEATH=MONEY

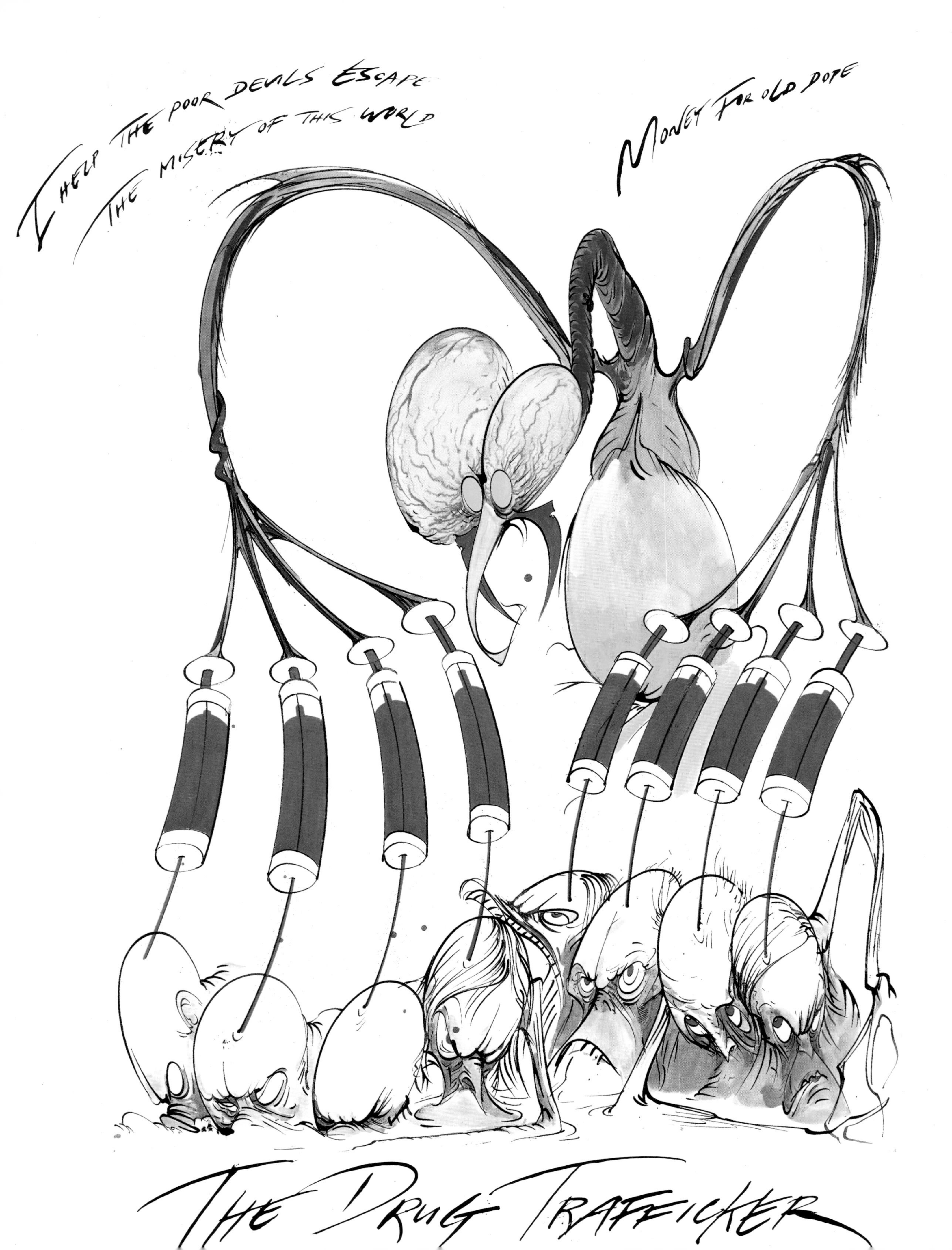
I HELP THE POOR DEVILS ESCAPE
THE MISERY OF THIS WORLD
MONEY FOR OLD DOPE
THE DRUG TRAFFICKER

Avarice
Where there's misery there's brass
The Drug Addict

THE MEDIA TYCOON

Avarice

It's understandable — this greedy swine
With his multi billions can never get enough
He must own more - control more more more more

What's it take to be really starving?

The Journalist

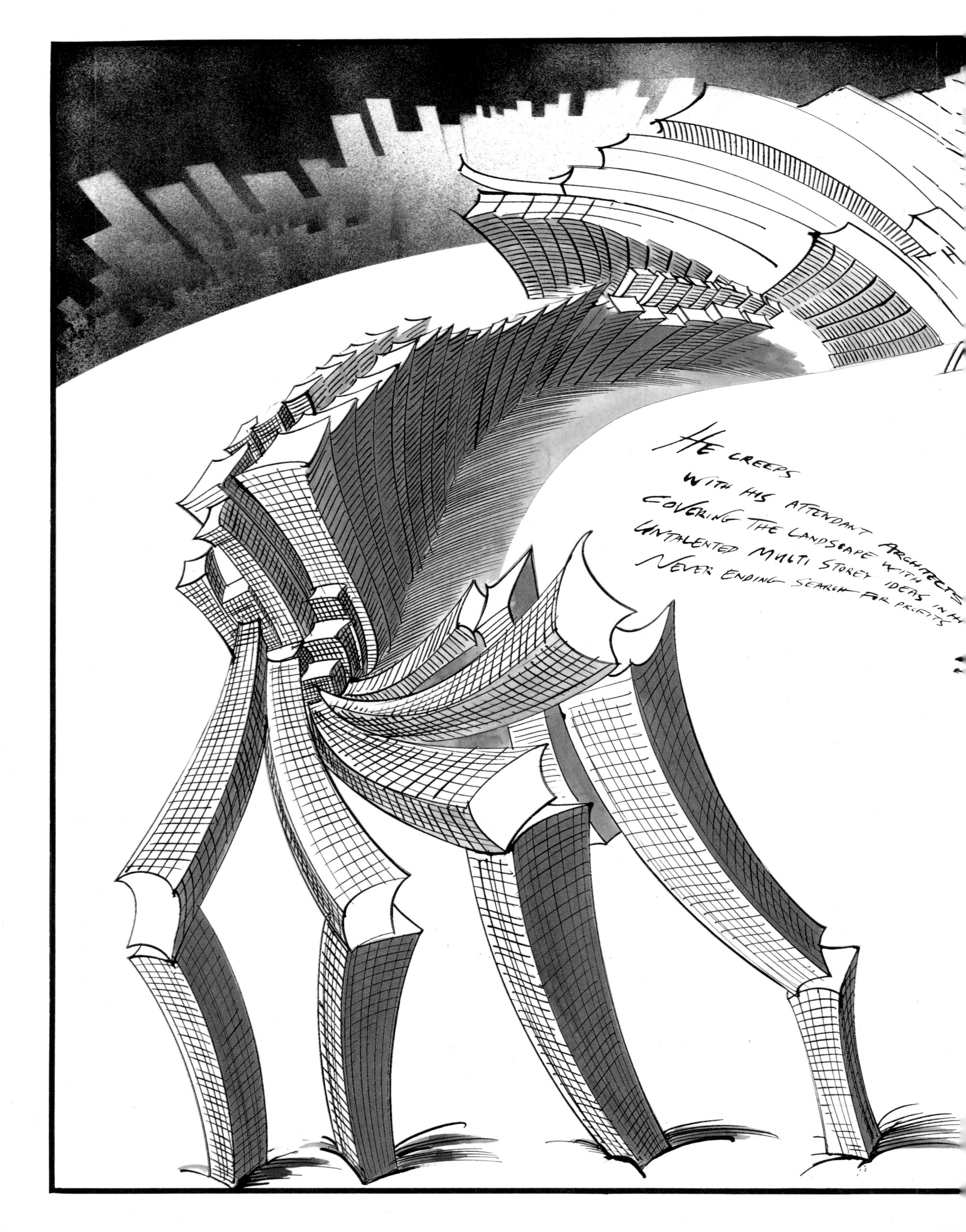
HE CREEPS
WITH HIS ATTENDANT ARCHITECTS
COVERING THE LANDSCAPE WITH
UNTALENTED MULTI STOREY IDEAS IN
NEVER ENDING SEARCH FOR PROFITS

OW SAD! HOW SAD!!
ONE HUNDRED AND NINETY FIVE POUNDS PLEASE
THE LAWYER AND HIS CLIENT

THOSE WHO HAVE MOST GET MORE

THE FINANCIER

Pride
PRIDE COMES BEFORE A FALL

GOD IS ON OUR SIDE
TAKE THAT

GOD IS WITH US.
AND THAT GROUND.
THE FLAG

PRIDE IN APPEARANCE

AREN'T THEY GORGEOUS? DRESSED IN THE CORPSES OF SEVERAL ENDANGERED SPECIES TO ENHANCE THEIR AIR OF STUPID SELF ESTEEM

DARLING YOU LOOK BLOODY!

Pride in Beauty
The Cosmetic Surgeon's Art

Before

Face Lift
Breast Lift
Stomach Lift
Bottom Lift

Try to put the clock bac[k]

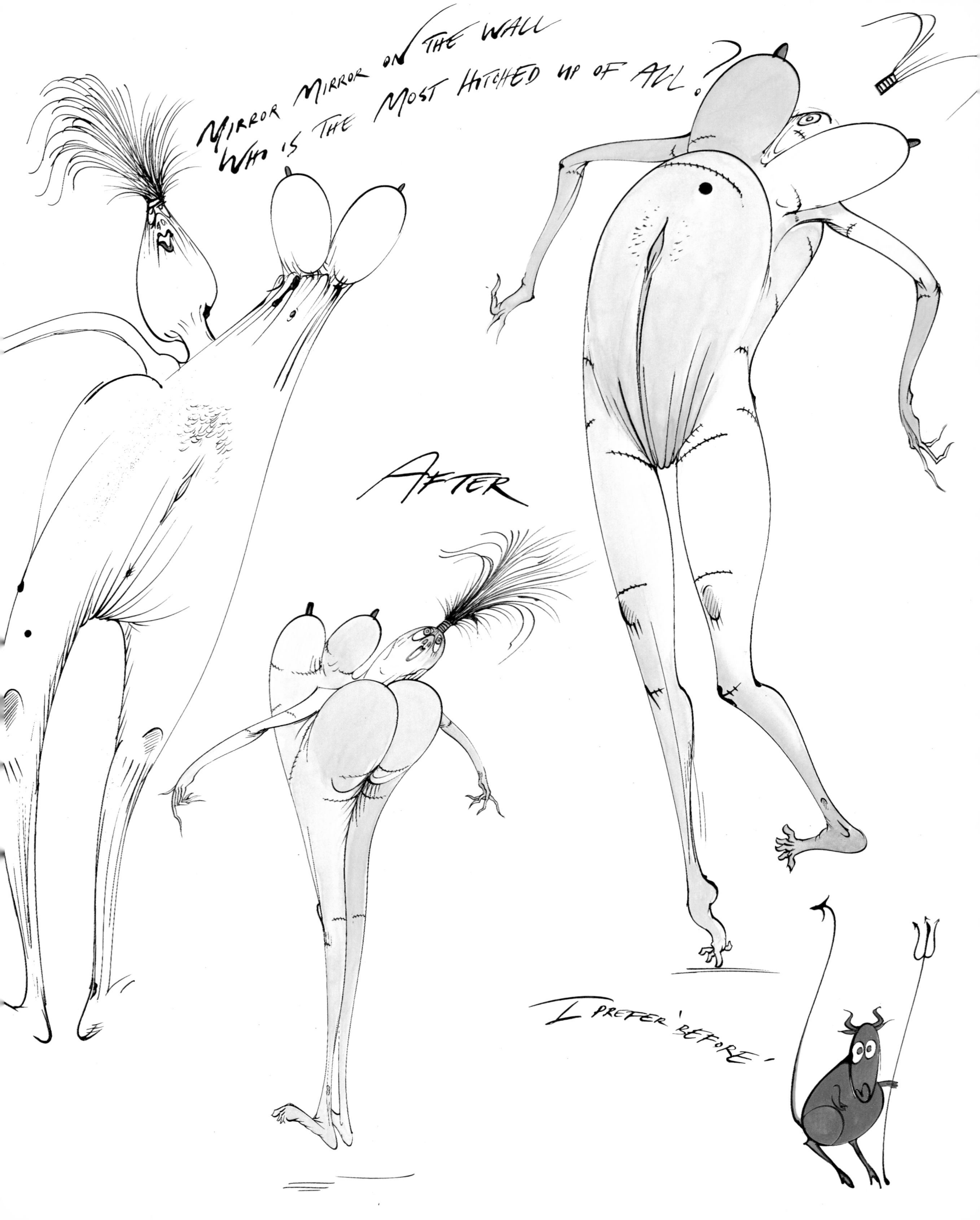
MIRROR MIRROR ON THE WALL
WHO IS THE MOST HITCHED UP OF ALL?
AFTER
I PREFER 'BEFORE'

PRIDE IN HIS OWN IMPORTANCE

A REAL —

HE'S SPRAYING AGAIN

IN HEROIC MEMORY OF AN INCREDIBLY CRUEL AND STUPID FOOL WHO WAS RESPONSIBLE FOR THE DEATH OF 19,628 YOUNG MEN
THE THING IS THESE
PEOPLE REALLY DO KNOW
WHAT
THE PROUD SOLDIER

THE PROUD CHURCHES

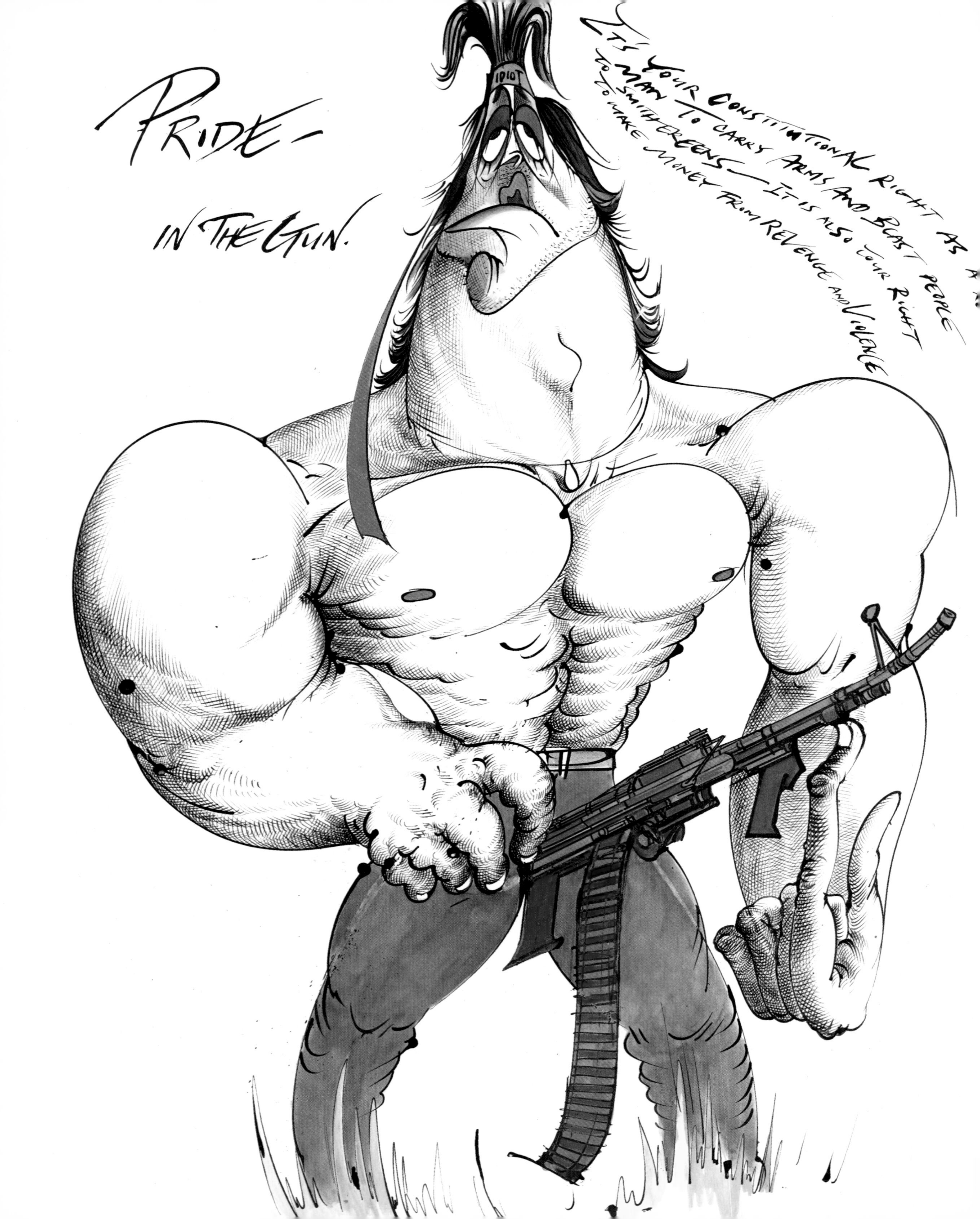
PRIDE -
IN THE GUN.
IDIOT
IT'S YOUR CONSTITUTIONAL RIGHT AS
MAN TO CARRY ARMS AND BLAST PEOPLE
TO SMITHEREENS — IT IS ALSO YOUR RIGHT
TO MAKE MONEY FROM REVENGE AND VIOLENCE

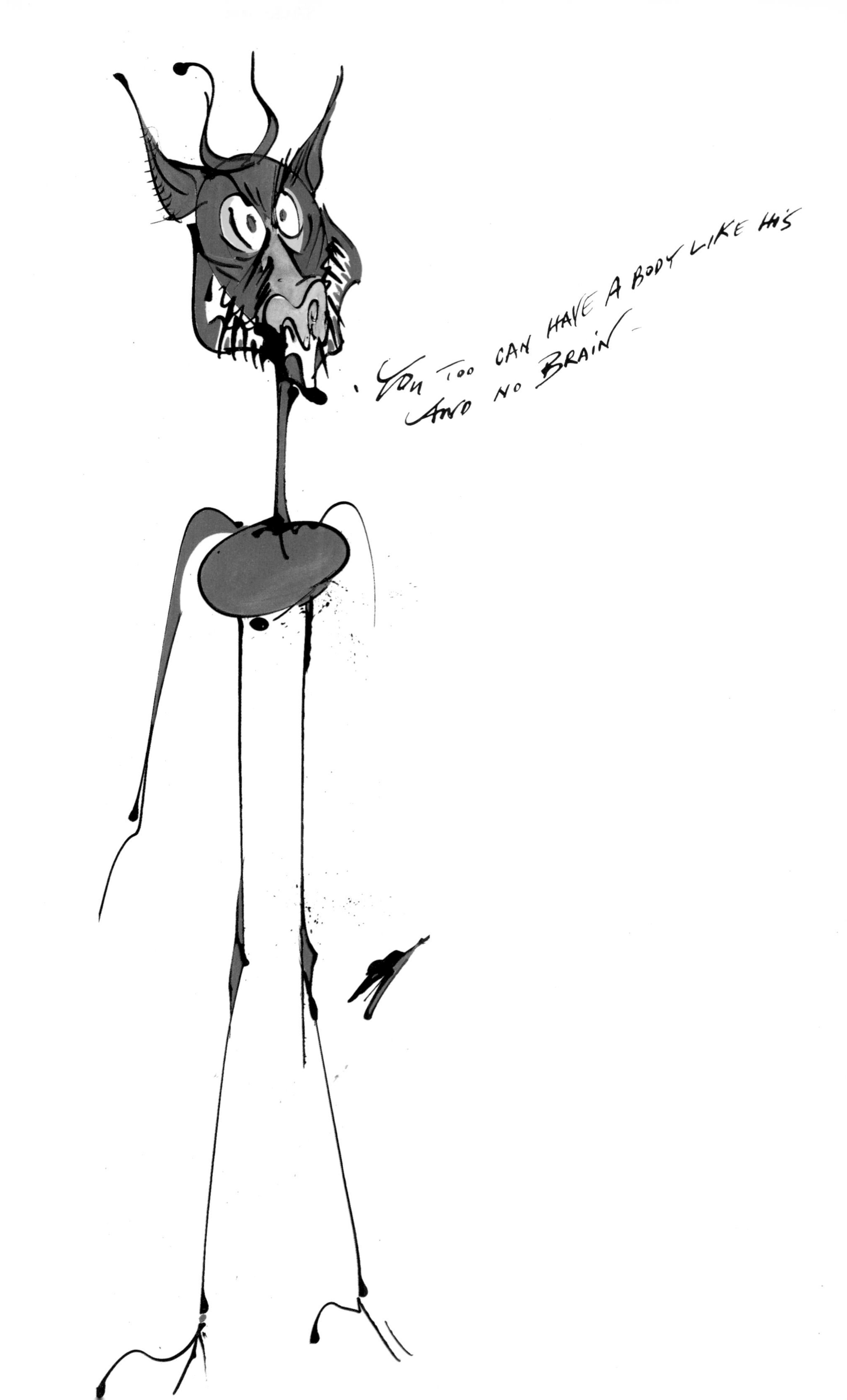
'You too can have a body like his
and no brain'

PRIDE IN WISDOM
OVER HIS FELLOWS

Envy

ENVY

Envy

I HOPE IT DOESN'T GO OFF PREMATURELY

ENVY OF A BIGGER ONE

Envy

KEEPING UP WITH THE JONES'S

SECOND HOUSE
PAYMENTS
HOUSE
TAX
MORTGAGE
TAX
SECOND MORTGAGE
TAX
WORRY WORRY WORRY
SCHOOLS
HOLIDAY ABROAD
CAR
SECOND MORTGAGE
SECOND CAR
HIRE PURCHASE PAYMENTS
TAX
ETC, ETC, ETC
I'VE GOT A FLAMING HEADACHE!

Envy

ENVY OF THE WRONG VALUES

THE FILM GODDESS
NOTHING
SEX
JEWELRY
GORGEOUS CLOTHES
JEWELRY
Diamonds
Rings
JEWELRY
SEX
HI!
INSINCERITY
Emeralds Rubies Gold
PROP
MONEY
SEX
MONEY
GORGEOUS
SEX
ISN'T SHE
ADMIRE HER
PLASTIC REPRESENTATION OF LIFE
SHE'S MADE ENTIRELY OF CARDBOARD
SHE'S SEXY
DON'T YOU WANT TO
EVERYTHING
I WANT TO BE
ENVY
IF ONLY I COULD BE LIKE HER
SHE'S
GOD HOW I
WOULDN'T YOU LIKE TO BE HER
I WORSHIP THE
ISN'T SHE
TAWDRY
MARVELOUS
LOOK AT HER
ENVY

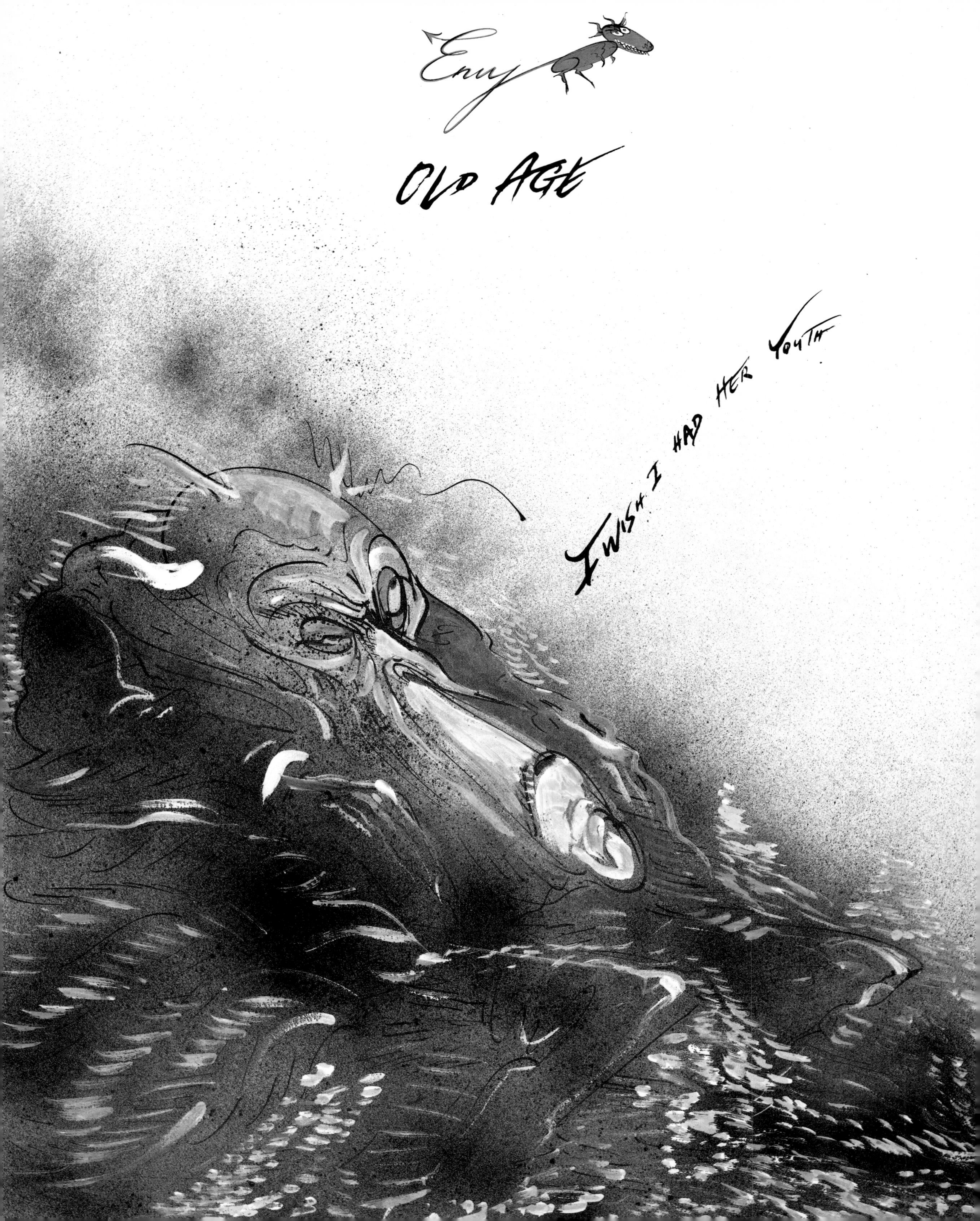
Envy
OLD AGE
I WISH I HAD HER YOUTH

I WISH I HAD HIS MONEY
YOUTH

Envy

OOOH! IF ONLY I HAD GUCCI SHOES
EVERTHING WOULD BE ALRIGHT

Sloth
SLOTH
A LAZY DEVIL

ENFORCED SLOTH

MODERN TECHNOLOGY GIVES YOU SO MUCH MORE LEISURE TIME TO STAND IN THE DOLE QUEUE

Sloth

ISN'T IT MARVELLOUS TO HAVE
HORROR IN YOUR OWN HOME

THE T.V. WATCHER

Sloth

Destruction of Species

ALL OUT
ACID RAIN
FORESTATION
DON'T WORRY WHAT CAN YOU DO ABOUT IT!
THE TORTURED EARTH

Sloth

SLOTH –
THE T.V. WATCHER
LIFE SUBSTITUTE

Anger

MY CAUSE
AT
ANY COST

You see there is no other way
For him to get his way —
But to blow up and tear u
Women and children

THE TERR·OR·IST

Anger

ANGER
THE MOTORIST

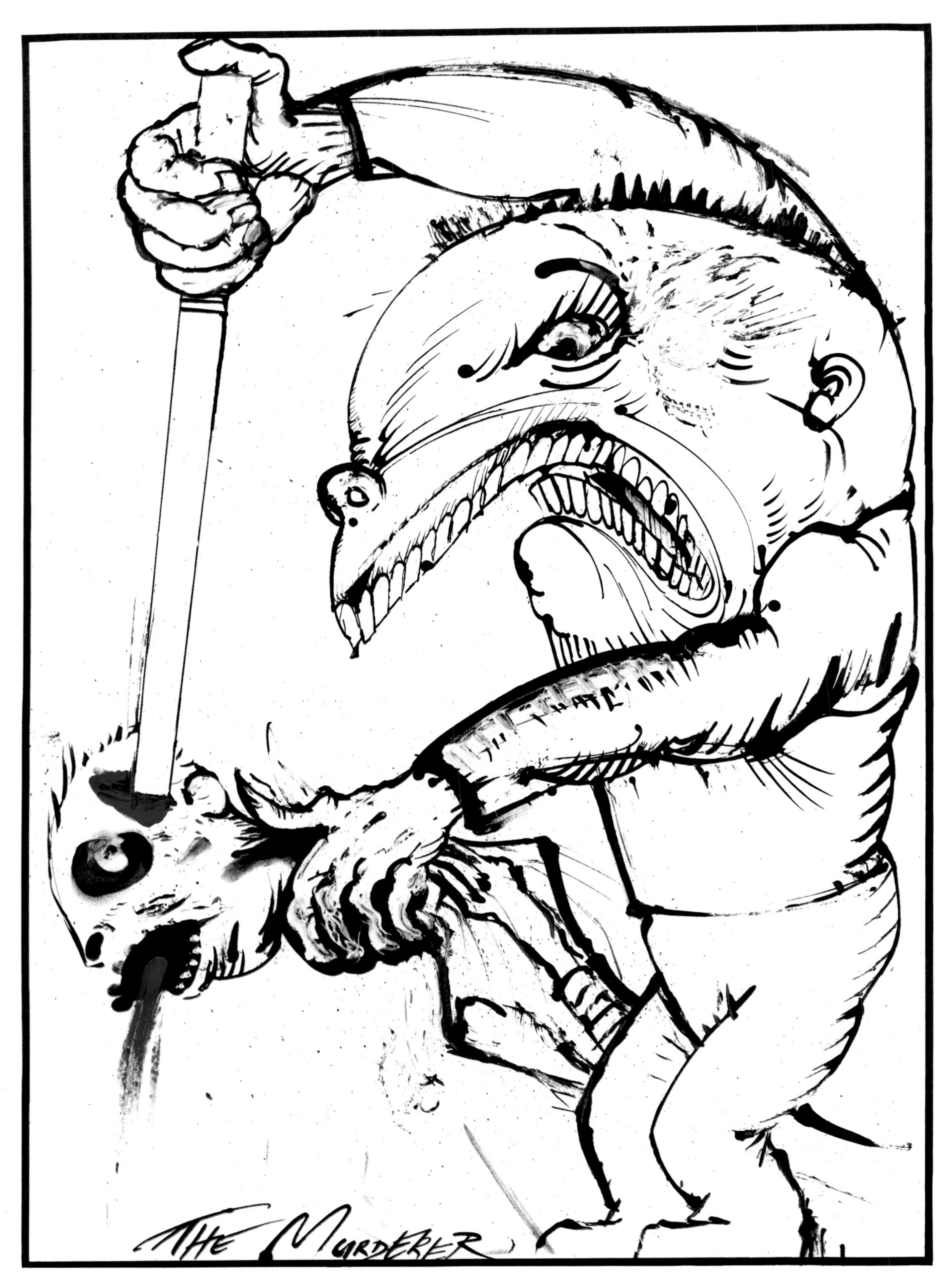

SPOT THE

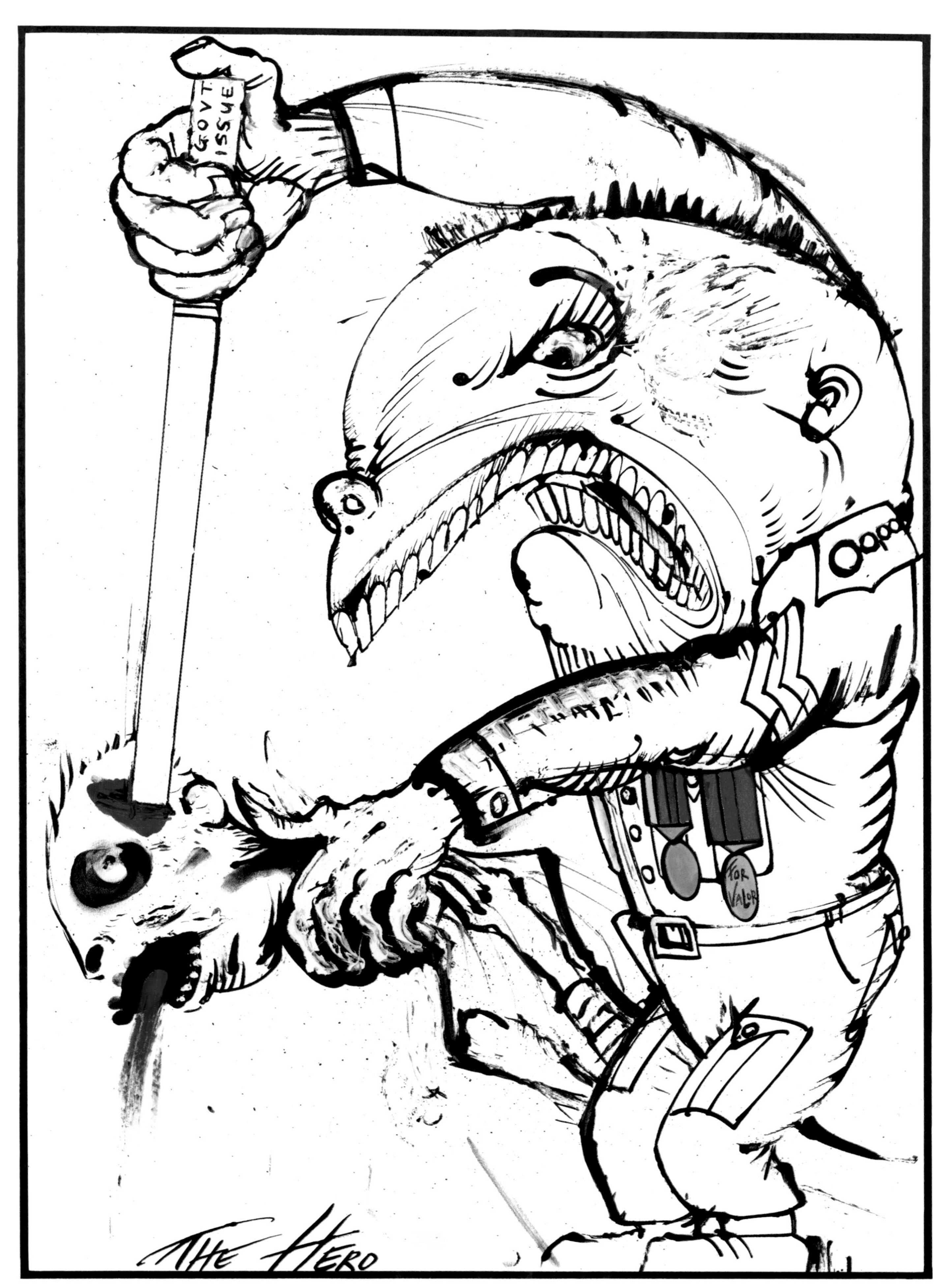

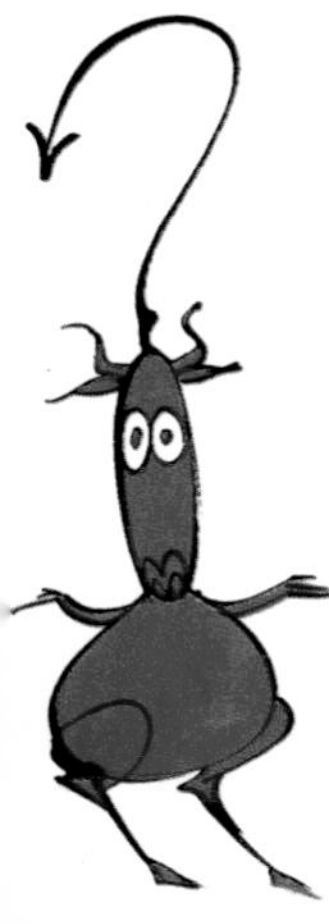

DIFFERENCE

Anger

THE ARMS RACE

Anger

DON'T WORRY
IT COULD N'T HAPPEN

WHITE HOUSE
BLUNDER

CHEERIO

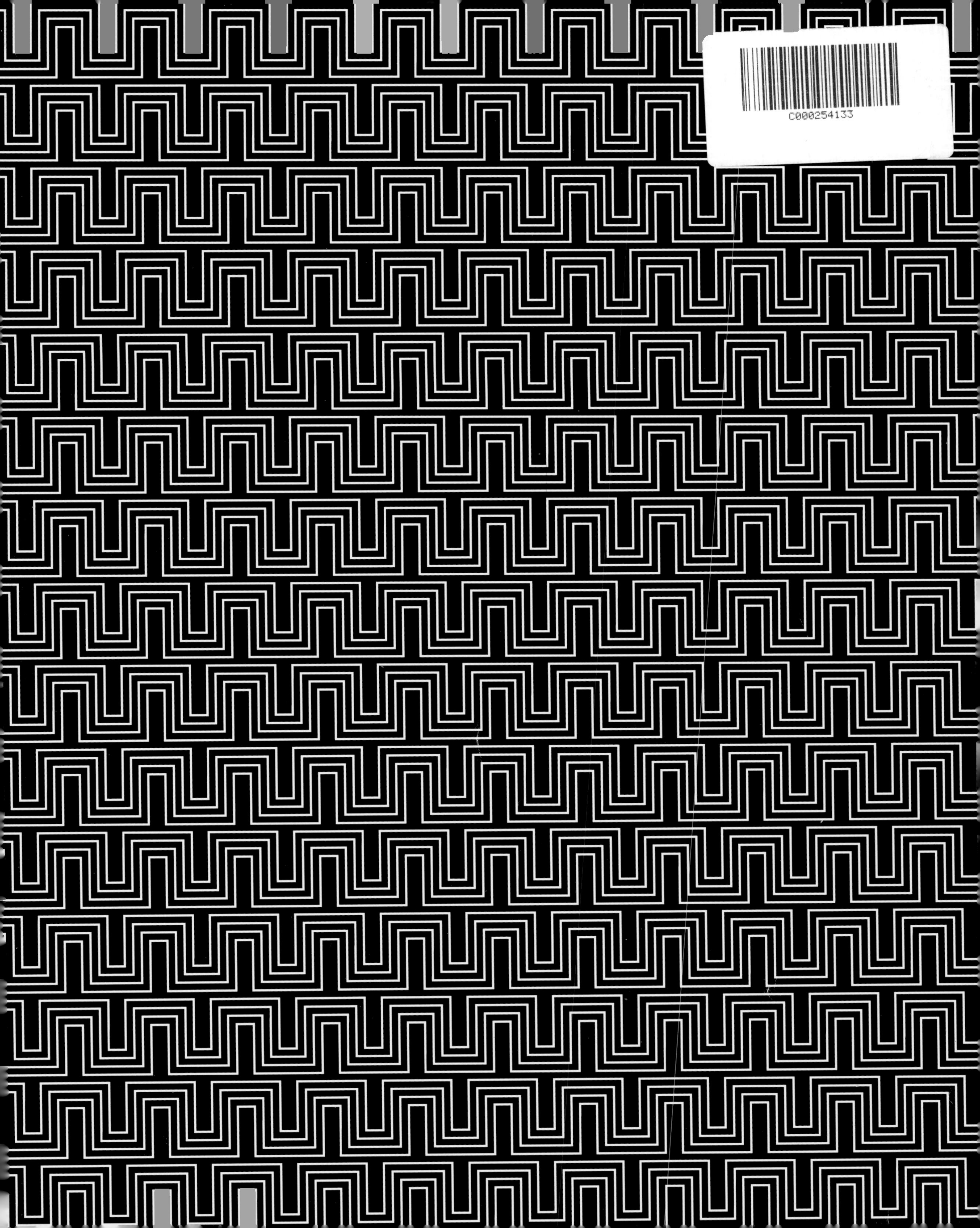
C000254133

THE TAILORED INTERIOR

INSPIRED INTERIORS SUZANNE KASLER

THE TAILORED INTERIOR

GREG NATALE

FOREWORD BY JONATHAN ADLER
PHOTOGRAPHY BY ANSON SMART

hardie grant books
MELBOURNE • LONDON

INTRODUCTION

I remember the sofa well. It was a walnut-stained timber with pink velvet upholstery, part of a set with matching armchairs, in the reproduction Baroque style my parents loved. It was dark, heavy and uninspiring – and it had to go.

I was fifteen years old and an expert on matters of taste. What were my parents thinking? It was the '80s, after all, the time of post-modernist Italian design group Memphis, with its vivid colours and quirky geometrics. Baroque repro had no place in my vision of the world, so I paid for an ad in the local classifieds and tried to get rid of the offending piece. My mother had no idea until people started ringing to ask about the sofa for sale – it seems not everyone had embraced the Memphis message.

Needless to say, the ad was withdrawn. The sofa may have won that round, but, while I never again attempted to sell any of my parents' pieces, I didn't give up trying to redecorate their house. I spent a whole summer holiday ripping down the bamboo wallpaper in one of their sitting rooms and repainting the walls pink. Did I mention it was the '80s, after all?

I think it's safe to say I wasn't your average child. Growing up in the Sydney suburbs, a son of Italian immigrants with four sisters, I'd had a strong sense of fashion and décor from an early age. Back then, a lot of my inspirations came from television – we didn't travel much, so I explored the world through what I saw on the screen. I was obsessed with the American series *Dynasty* and thought Alexis Carrington's all-white apartment, with its pops of pink, the height of glamour. And I know I'm not the only fan of that glass desk with tusks for legs that stood proudly in her office. I remember watching the film *2001: A Space Odyssey* and being blown away by the images – the shot of a French-style room with an illuminated floor is still etched in my mind.

Of course, these fictional interiors didn't necessarily inspire my particular style, but they motivated me to want to create my own amazing spaces. I'd seen what was possible with vision and imagination. My eldest sister, a fashion designer, was the first person to put a pencil in my hand and from that point I never looked back.

Once I had the choice, it made sense to focus my studies on design and art. I did a three-year course in interior design at the Design Centre Enmore, in Sydney, after which I went on to study visual arts at Sydney College of the Arts and architecture at the University of Technology. In 1996, I got my first break in a residential design firm as a junior interior designer. That initial job in the industry is the hardest to get and I knew how lucky I was to be doing what I loved and studying as I went. From there, I worked in two more commercial firms, where I learned the art of drawing plans and the importance of discipline. For those outside the industry, interior design is what they see in the end result, all free spirit and creativity, but few realise what a highly technical and detail-oriented field it is.

In 2001, I started my own business, Greg Natale Design. It was a time of change in the design industry – the previous decade had been dominated by minimalism, in which white 'boxes' and bare walls prevailed. Now, designers were looking towards a more layered effect, which couldn't have suited me better. I have a great deal of affection for minimalism and value its strengths in creating a blank canvas upon which to style a room, but I wanted something more. I was in my late twenties, a child of the 'excess era', and I wanted a look that was luxurious and warm.

I knew that, to be noticed, I needed to do something out of the ordinary, so I began exploring the patterns, prints and textures that I'd admired in my childhood and building them up over minimalist foundations. Fusing the two came to be my signature look. I found inspiration in the work of icons such as the late English designer David Hicks. His approach was always clean, but I loved his use of bold colours and the way he mixed straight and classic lines, layering them with geometric patterns. Discovering the creations of

Danish designer Verner Panton was also a turning point for my career. His style of building up entire environments, repeating patterns on floors, walls and ceilings, has had a great influence on my aesthetic.

My first job under my own name was not a grand house, but my sister Sarina's one-bedroom apartment. Little did I know what a big deal this would end up being. She wanted something rich and sumptuous, so I took what was basically a small box and installed wall-to-wall custom-coloured wallpaper by Florence Broadhurst, layering it with matching artwork and linen. After the apartment was published in Australia's prestigious interior design magazine *Belle* in 2002 and the UK's iconic *Wallpaper** magazine in 2005, people started to sit up and take notice of my work. It was the uniqueness of this project that won me my first award, the 2002 Belle Wild Card award, a category created for me.

My inspirations are many and varied, but fashion has always been a first love. Designers such as Halston and Tom Ford each defined the look of such different decades, yet I admire the way that both have perfected timeless tailoring coupled with a refined sexiness. Outside the world of fashion, I am influenced by art, film and travel. When I first saw the pyramid extension to the Louvre Museum in Paris as an ambitious twenty-year-old, I was mesmerised by the contrast between old and new. In my own industry, I've always been a fan of the Californian Case Study Houses of the '50s and '60s, commissioned by the influential US *Arts & Architecture* magazine, and of the dynamic, sculptural work of American modernist architect Paul Rudolph.

My own Italian heritage reveals its influence in my love of fabrics, prints and textures. The irony is not lost on me that I spent all that time tearing down my parents' bamboo-print wallpaper when I was younger, only to become known for my use of patterned wallpaper today! In the same spirit, I showed my parents there were no hard feelings about that sofa by featuring one of their matching Baroque chairs in my first apartment – a bit of personal history with a touch of humour. I also installed a Murano glass chandelier as a fond homage to my late aunt, who adored it. I love the idea of reinventing something from another decade and making it work in a new environment. We respond to the familiar, after all.

It's that familiar, personal element, which I believe is the key to a successful interior. In my industry, it's all very well to be on-trend, but what gives a design longevity and meaning is the connection it makes with people. I take care to inject my client's personality into each project I work on, which ensures that the place will remain significant to them. I was just as careful to bring my personality and passions to my own apartment. The same goes for anyone decorating their home – if you put yourself into the piece, it will always be special to you.

With this book, I want to share some of the lessons I've learnt while creating interiors. I know many people find the process daunting – where do you even begin? How do you harness your ideas and turn them into an achievable reality? How do you deal with the demands of different spaces to get the look you want? What many don't realise is that there's a great deal of commonsense and quite a few useful rules that can be applied to building successful spaces. I'd like to illustrate some of them here.

These pages offer a window on my work and an insight into my approach – how I tackle the design process, from establishing a starting point, through to tips on working with paint, wallpaper, proportion, contrast, balance, colour and pattern, to the 'fun' part of adding the finishing touches and achieving a complete, cohesive look.

I've titled this book *The Tailored Interior* for two reasons. Firstly, because of that essentially bespoke element of interior design – creating a successful space is all about capturing the vision and passions of the owner. It's about making your mark. Secondly, because my own style is very tailored and tightly edited – I believe in building a space in which every piece has a place, every combination an explanation. My approach is layered and considered, with a love of monochrome, a penchant for pattern, and a touch of drama. I hope that, by sharing some of my work and a few of my thoughts, I can help to inspire anyone venturing into the world of interior design.

Previous page *Here, I am standing in the lounge room of an Edwardian house that I restored in Croydon, Sydney. The collection of black and white Fornasetti plates stands out against the soft blue walls, while referencing the monochrome palette and Fornasetti designs that appear elsewhere in the house.*

Opposite *I am known for my love of pattern on pattern, and my sister Sarina's apartment in Sydney's Summer Hill – my first job – allowed me to express this. In her bedroom, I took Florence Broadhurst's Steps III print, customised the colour and turned it upside down in the wallpaper, blinds and bed linen to create a fully layered effect, offset by a framed detail of the print itself.*

THE STARTING POINT

When I was studying interior design, identifying the starting point of any project was always the hardest part. Where do you begin when you're faced with a huge blank canvas? How do you move on from an existing design to create a fresh approach? With experience, I've found that these questions don't change, but the answers – and how to find them – do become somewhat easier.

Back then, we students were encouraged to start by creating a sculpture – not of a house, or room, but rather a small abstract piece that captured a certain mood. While I'm not suggesting you go out and buy modelling clay, this exercise illustrates an important point about getting started. This stage is about finding the mood you want for your space and you're looking for any inspiration that will assist you in that process.

A few questions to consider first: does the location offer its own inspiration? For example, does a coastal house call for a laid-back, breezy vibe; would a country homestead be enhanced by a warm, rustic interior? What about the house itself: are you working with an existing building? If so, perhaps architectural or period elements could suggest a way forward. Or do you have a completely blank canvas? It's a wonderfully appealing prospect but can be overwhelming. In this case, do you have a favourite piece of furniture or art that may set the tone for your new space? Inspiration can begin anywhere, but it's this starting point, however minimal, that helps keep you on track because you can always refer back to it.

FINDING YOUR INSPIRATION

The architecture of a house can provide a strong starting point. For a contemporary house we built in Brisbane, Queensland, the sharply angled roof provided the perfect inspiration for how we would approach the interior design. We echoed the defined lines of the roof inside the house by introducing various square, triangle, diagonal and chevron patterns into the wallpaper, tiles, panelling and even the timber treatment on doors and windows. The palette shifts between black and white, yet remains linked by pattern, and the effect is eye-catching, with the lines creating a dynamic interplay throughout.

Ask yourself if the bones of your house already have something to offer. Are there angles, lines, shapes you could echo through interior finishes? Does the period of the house suggest a certain ambience you could accentuate?

Sometimes, it's a favourite piece of furniture that sets the scene. Two of my clients in a sprawling country house in Geelong, Victoria, were keen to build a look around their antique dining table and chairs, which were upholstered in black leather. Such a striking combination couldn't help but determine the tone for the space. The scheme for the dining room became dark and moody as a result, with the furniture strong enough to allow a dramatic use of black-on-black chevron wallpaper without being consumed by it.

In my first apartment in East Sydney it was a trio of vintage black mirror coffee tables that started off my design. I'd scrounged enough money to be able to buy them at auction and built my living room around their moody gleam. Those tables are treasured possessions that have become part of a collection I will keep forever.

We're sentimental creatures and most of us have at least one piece of furniture that we're not willing to part with. If you intend to make that piece a feature in your design, you need to take a good look at it. Does the piece suggest a particular mood that will suit your idea for the new space? Could it influence some of your palette choices? Will it dictate what other furniture sits with it? Or is it actually restricting your design ideas? In this case, all that may be required is a makeover to refresh the piece and keep it relevant. Don't be afraid to rethink the role of old favourites – simply moving a piece of furniture to a different part of the house can create a completely new statement, just as re-upholstering a chair or sofa can contribute to a different design concept while giving that much-loved piece a new lease of life.

Artworks are often among the existing elements that need to be taken into consideration as we move from one space into another. In one inner-city Melbourne house the number, and even the size, of the owner's artworks required forethought when we were planning the design. Luckily, the house's

Previous page *In this house in Melbourne the stunning gold artwork on the wall was the starting point for the living room design. Here, accents of gold punctuate a palette of charcoal, mauve and burgundy to create a moody, opulent space.*

Opposite *An antique dining table and black leather-upholstered chairs set the scene for a darkly glamorous dining room in this country house in Geelong, Victoria. The black-on-black wallpaper and grey-painted panelling work with the furniture to enhance the intimate, sophisticated mood.*

Above *The vibrant hues of Andy Warhol's* Marilyn *screenprint provided the starting point for the colour choices I made in my current apartment in Sydney's Darlinghurst. Beneath it, a Bertoia chair by Knoll and a Kelly Wearstler Trapezoid sculpture encapsulate the apartment's monochrome scheme.*

Right *I echoed the print's bright tones in a painting by Australian artist Scott Petrie and a pink feature chair, adding further hits of colour through accessories.*

Opposite and above *The blues and whites of New England classic styling merge with Asian-influenced patterns to create a treasure trove of local and international pieces. The sense of old-world travel and adventure is highlighted by eclectic additions such as a stack of pre-loved suitcases and a model sailing ship (opposite).*

Above and opposite *The sharp angles of the roof of this contemporary house in Brisbane were the inspiration for the use of lines and geometrics throughout. Chevron timber treatments on the doors at one entrance provide a striking focal point.*

Next page *The sofa was the starting point for the study in the Geelong country house. After having it re-upholstered, I mirrored its long, low form with the coffee table, adding two little antique side tables. Balancing the horizontal arrangement is a series of vintage illustrations of jockeys from Vanity Fair, one of many equine elements that reference the house's function as part of a horse stud farm.*

The Horse Whisperer

Opposite *Artworks feature prominently around the grand entrance of this Melbourne house. The vast walls allow them to be displayed to great effect, while the large reception room picks up their monochromatic scheme.*

Above *The owner had a number of artworks for which we needed to find suitable spaces. On the upstairs landing I used a pair of Porta Romana benches to anchor two large pieces, offering a pleasant resting spot.*

Next page *Two inspirations came together in one room of this Edwardian house in Croydon – the client wanted a library and we'd just purchased four mid-century William Haines chairs. They fit the space perfectly.*

One of the inspiring things about interior design is that it allows you to bring some humour to a space. The addition of wallpaper that light-heartedly references a room's purpose offers a bit of fun as well as function.

MY
READING
LIFE
BOB
RAISING
2 UNIT

INTERIOR ARCHITECTURE

When creating a space, I like to think in terms of a trilogy. The first component, interior architecture, refers to the walls, floors and ceilings; the second component, design, to the joinery, bathrooms and kitchens, lighting, layout and doors; and the third, decoration, to the loose furniture, rugs and accessories. All three must work together to achieve a cohesive look, but in this chapter, I intend to address the first component.

Since its early days, my studio has always worked on elements of interior architecture, such as remodelling and building extensions. Today, we build whole houses from scratch. I think it's the perfectionist in me who wants to get everything right, down to the foundations of a room. And it's essential that we do get this stage right. I'm not talking about huge jobs such as pulling down walls – perfecting the foundations of a room can be as simple as a fresh coat of paint and some new flooring.

The walls, floors and ceilings – a mini trilogy of their own – are your canvas, the first step after you've established your concept. They provide the backdrop for everything that follows. The order in which you approach them isn't all that important, as long as you stay focused on your concept. This may hark back to my '80s TV education, but I tend to visualise a room like a spaceship, where the flow between walls, floor and ceiling is so moulded and seamless you don't notice the edges. Analogy aside, it's that seamlessness you're aiming for when you look at the interior architecture.

WALLS – YOUR GREAT CANVAS

First, take a look at what is already there and the state it's in – features such as panelling, skirting, cornicing, picture rails, fireplaces. If the features are in place, my recommendation is that you restore rather than remove. You can always add other elements such as moulding to continue the look, provided they are in keeping with your original concept.

Arches make a statement as a way of connecting spaces. In a house in Sydney's Bellevue Hill we installed a large arch leading from the entrance to the living room, repeating it in smaller versions around the space. Similarly, one of the original features we restored in an Edwardian house in Croydon was an arch in the vestibule that led into the formal living room. We created a series of arches around it, opening the vestibule onto other rooms and making it the core of the house. The style was in keeping with the house's design but the new layout was more spacious.

Next, consider what finish you want on the walls. Paint is the number one way to make a big difference to a room, creating a vast and consistent canvas upon which to layer your design. My advice is that, unless you're a real pro at painting, it is worth investing in a good painter. You'll regret a bad paint job far more – and for far longer – than you would spending the money on getting it done properly in the first place.

I am particularly fond of white walls and white skirting boards, a combination I find simple and clean, although occasionally contrasting colours can really lift a space. In the Croydon house we used white paint for all the woodwork – the skirtings, mouldings and architraves – and introduced a soft powder-blue for the walls in formal areas.

There are times when the walls can work a little harder in the room. An apartment in Sydney's Elizabeth Bay features black-stained oak walls that serve a second role as cabinets – a stylish solution we installed to maximise space. In a large modern residence in Tennyson Point we created a feature wall out of the same concrete bricks that were part of the house's exterior. It provided a textural contrast to the white interior, while maintaining a link with the architecture of the house.

If you're tempted to introduce different colours in a couple of rooms, remember that those rooms still need to flow and exhibit some level of cohesion – perhaps using a consistent skirting board colour or lighting style between them could achieve this. And, with all paint choices, apply swatches to your walls so you can observe how they vary in different lights.

Not everyone wants a blank canvas and wallpaper can make a room sing. There are factors to consider, such as the colours you intend to use, the scale of the pattern in relation to the size of the room, the style of the design and whether it suits other details in the room. Many worry that wallpaper makes a room appear smaller, but that isn't necessarily the case. I believe it can work its magic in mysterious ways, making a large room look cosier, while enhancing the possibilities of a small room.

Previous page *The dining room of an apartment in Sydney's Elizabeth Bay displays a clever use of space, with the timber walls doubling as cabinets. A coffer in the ceiling delineates the area, lending focus to the striking lights and dining setting below.*

Opposite *Juxtaposing the black of the marble floors and staircase of a house in Bellevue Hill, Sydney, the white-painted walls and ceilings visually heighten and expand the space. The use of arches and panelling proves a white wall choice needn't be plain.*

AUDREY HEPBURN

Many people are hesitant about using dark colours for walls, but it is entirely possible – and pleasingly dramatic – to embrace dark walls, wallpaper and even ceilings as long as you have sufficient natural light.

Previous page *In the country house in Geelong, Victoria, the light from the stained-glass bay windows plays on the patterns of my Porter's Paints chevron wallpaper, rug and the timber surfaces, enriching the dark palette.*

Opposite *A vaulted, slatted ceiling in the pool room of this contemporary Brisbane house lifts, lightens and elongates the room, drawing the eye outside so interior and exterior seem to merge. The rug contributes by echoing the form of the pavers outside.*

Above *This country house in Sutton Forest, in the NSW Southern Highlands, offered the chance for a fresh take on a classic design. V-jointed timber panelling enhances the angles of the conservatory, with the white-painted surfaces allowing the view to dominate.*

Above *In the Sutton Forest kitchen a play on exposed beams suits the country house style, while the white paint juxtaposed with the glamorous black cabinetry and intricately designed island bench gives the space a modern edge.*

Opposite *A similar treatment features in the loft-like ceiling of the Geelong country house, with the white-painted beams offset by the rustic, textural details of the butcher's tiles on the walls and Turkish terrazzo tiles on the floor.*

Opposite *A three-level metal screen alongside the staircase makes a stunning vertical statement in the contemporary Brisbane house, balancing the length of white walls and providing another layer of detail.*

Above *In the entrance to the home theatre room my Porter's Paints white-on-white striped wallpaper maintains the neutral palette while adding interest. In dramatic contrast, an onyx feature slab almost glows with warmth.*

Next page *Natural light in the Elizabeth Bay apartment offsets the black cabinets and charcoal stucco walls.*

VANITAS
Gianni Versace
Do not disturb

PROPORTION

It was the final year of my interior design course and I was due to present my project to the panel of examiners, one of whom was the award-winning, New Zealand-born Australian architect Ian Moore. The honour was high but so were the nerves. We'd been tasked with designing a whole boutique hotel, and I distinctly remember my living room – all white, birch, plywood and pops of orange. Moore liked it all except for one important element. I'd got the proportion completely wrong, having chosen furniture that was too small for the space and consequently became lost in it. This was a turning point for me and I suppose I'm lucky to have learned the lesson so early in my career. Since then, I have always recognised the significant role proportion plays in design.

In my work, proportion is about bringing everything back to the human scale – helping people to feel they are comfortable in a space, no matter what its size, because they can relate to it. The notion of human scale has been a focus of architects for decades. Back in the '40s, French modernist icon Le Corbusier tried to create a system of proportions based on the Modulor, a stylised human figure of a man with one arm raised. Le Corbusier's theory was that using this system would ensure the creation of architecture and design that was consistently pleasing to the eye. While its success has been much debated, there is no doubt that its greatest achievement was in placing people at the core of design.

Our clients may not see the theories behind the process, nor do they need to, but the result should always be the same: a welcoming space in which they feel comfortable. Proportion applies to everything, from the size of the fireplace, to how much furniture you have and how big it is, to the number of lights, to the scale of pattern on your wallpaper … what's essential is working in harmony with the relevant room.

WORKING WITH LARGE SPACES

WALLS AND CEILINGS

In a big area, obviously you're going to be facing an expanse of wall and ceiling space. A picture rail can help to break up a wall and bring down a high ceiling to a more human scale. In the same way, a beautiful pendant light hanging from the ceiling, or some floor-to-ceiling curtains, serves to visually draw the ceiling closer to you.

In a vast, all-white space, timber panelling is a way to break up the expanse of walls, as well as preventing the palette choice from appearing too bland. If you are painting or wallpapering your walls, a darker colour paint or wallpaper with a larger pattern can make a room feel more intimate. The ceilings of the large, classic guesthouse in Brisbane brought particular challenges of proportion and consistency – they were high, but in some rooms the roof cut into them, altering the angles significantly. We used the picture rails as our consistent line throughout and ran a horizontal band of navy blue wallpaper through the house from chair rail to picture rail, which served the dual purpose of bringing the ceilings down a little while keeping a cohesive look, even in the more unorthodox rooms.

Sometimes, adding panels of wallpaper can help to break up a vast wall space. In the Melbourne house we introduced differently sized panels of grey grasscloth wallpaper to the dining room's white walls. It was a way to bring intimacy to the large room while staying consistent with the palette choices throughout the house.

Resolving a large wall area isn't always about applying paint or wallpaper. It's also an opportunity to display bigger pieces of art, or, if you have smaller artworks, to cluster several together. Shelving and bookshelves can also dilute the look of a long expanse of wall, while adding a personal decorative touch through the items you choose to display on them.

FURNITURE

Take it from me, you don't want your furniture getting lost in a large space! You'll definitely need bigger pieces and more of them to make sure the room feels full and prevent it from taking on that 'airport' look. This means upping the ante – and the budget – but the good news is you will have more freedom to play with choices.

When it comes to how much furniture to put in a room, I find that, far too often, people tend to err on the conservative side, forgetting that furniture can serve an ornamental function as well as a practical one. Furniture adds warmth, comfort, layers and personality – and so often a room can take more than you imagine, especially when it's a generous size. At the sprawling country house in Geelong, space allowed us to create double

Previous page *Plays on proportion are just as important in the smallest vignette as in an entire room. In the Melbourne house a standout star mirror presides over a simple mantelpiece display.*

Opposite *A double living room in the Geelong country house utilises the huge space and allows for differently purposed areas. Two brick-red Bolier sofas provide a dynamic sense of movement.*

RUGS – NEED TO KNOW

I'm a big fan of rugs and would like to share a few tips on where, why and how to place your rugs correctly.

Role The most important role a rug should play is to anchor the furniture in a room so it doesn't appear to 'float'. You can achieve this by placing the furniture directly on the rug or around it and just touching the edges.

Size The size of the rug should always be proportionate to the furniture – if you're in doubt, get a bigger rug and place your furniture on top of it.

Space A rug is a great way to visually create different 'zones' in open-plan living spaces, softly delineating areas while focusing the furniture around it.

Texture Rugs add warmth and interest to a room, creating an immediately cosier space and another design layer. Texture, colour and pattern are all considerations – on a patterned floor, try a textured rug; on a plain floor, use your rug to play with colour and/or prints.

Shape The shape you choose is up to you. Rectangular rugs are versatile choices for most rooms, but a round rug could provide a way to introduce organic curves into a room full of sharp angles.

Position Placing a rug under a dining table is a great decorative touch. A simple rule to keep in mind is that the rug should be 600 mm (23.5 inches) wider than the table on all sides.

Coverage In my opinion, hallways always need a runner. The hallway is so often a neglected area in decorating and, given that there's not a lot you can bring to it aside from artwork and lighting, an attractive, textural runner along the floor is an easy way to create a warm, welcoming statement.

Without the Ralph Lauren Sheldon rug, the study of the classic Brisbane guesthouse could have been an unwelcoming space, dominated by its flooring. The ample proportions of the rug anchor the trestle table and pendant light, while allowing a border of timber flooring to highlight the space. The effect is a room that appears warm, balanced and full.

Above *In the Melbourne house a large Arne Jacobsen Egg chair and two smaller pink Swan chairs present a play on proportion that's emphasised by the exaggerated lines of the Salvador Dali-designed floor lamp.*

Opposite *That vignette becomes part of many pieces that enrich the space in a living room sizeable enough to carry the sweeping curves of a Minotti Dubuffet sofa as well as two Adeline cocktail tables by Oly.*

Next page *The dining setting in this contemporary Brisbane house illustrates how the amount and size of the furniture you choose are key to resolving a large space. Two tall, white leather armchairs flank the long ebony dining table, breaking up the horizontal line created by the eight dining chairs covered in Hermès fabric. The armchairs and lighting reduce the vertical space, bringing table and ceiling closer.*

THE HERMÈS SCARF
History & Mystique
50 OF THE WORLD'S BEST APARTMENTS

C.S. LEWIS • A LIFE

Opposite *A four-poster Dorothy Draper bed is the hero of the Croydon house's main bedroom, its ebonised timber echoed in other pieces. The room's size means the bed's strong lines accentuate the softly hued walls, lights and rug rather than overpower them.*

Above *In the guest bedroom of this Sydney apartment the oversized pattern of the Pompeian wallpaper from Cole & Son works beautifully with the smaller pieces and softer tones around it to visually enhance the space.*

THE RACING GAME

Opposite and above *Grey walls and panelling in the Geelong country house bring an intimacy to the large living area. Here, every space has been utilised, such as a bay window that I turned into a reading nook by adding a dining table and two antique chairs. Throughout the room, I've using different groupings of furniture to create a connected series of cosy vignettes.*

Next page *Panels of grey grasscloth wallpaper break up the vast white walls of the dining room in the Melbourne house, bringing them closer to the human scale. The panels' soft finish offsets the gleam of the dining table and aged mirror feature on one wall.*

Large spaces provide the opportunity to introduce a variety of treatments – perhaps breaking up vast wall areas with panels, artworks and different finishes, or adding extra furniture and accessories.

Opposite *The exception to the rule: boldly patterned wallpaper doesn't always make a room look smaller. In the living room of this small one-bedroom apartment in Fitzroy the diagonal stripes of my wallpaper seem to elongate the walls, an effect heightened by the narrow portraits and low sofa and table.*

Above *In the bedroom, too, the diagonals give a sense of limitless space, enhanced by the verticals of the lamp and bedhead. A single-drawer bedside table shows you can have the pieces you want if you decrease the scale.*

S,M,L,XL

Opposite *A custom-made sideboard brings gilt elements to the living room of the Sydney apartment, together with the objects and mirror above. The patterned monochromes of a vintage-inspired rug anchor the room.*

Above *Gold adds a layer of luxe detail against the mosaic tiles in a powder room of the Clontarf house.*

Next page *Soft yet sculptural furniture, elegant wall finishes and a palette of charcoal, mauve and burnished golds highlighted by the accessories – the living room of the Melbourne house is sophisticated and inviting.*

If you start with a neutral-toned sofa, you can then add details, patterns and pops of colour through cushions and accessories. Textures provide another level to play with – mix soft and hard furnishings for dramatic effect.

Previous page *Black features prominently in the layers of the living room in this Elizabeth Bay apartment, receiving vitality through different treatments – the sheer curtains, the mirrored vintage Italian coffee tables from Habité in LA and the decadent fur carpet.*

Opposite *In the grand entrance of the Melbourne house, a Kelly Wearstler leather Soufflé chair and a Dorothy Draper Alcalá drinks table displaying a single ornament present a tightly edited focal point below the sweeping staircase.*

Above *Against the moody charcoal-grey backdrop, gilt elements in the living room create a visual 'conversation' between pieces.*

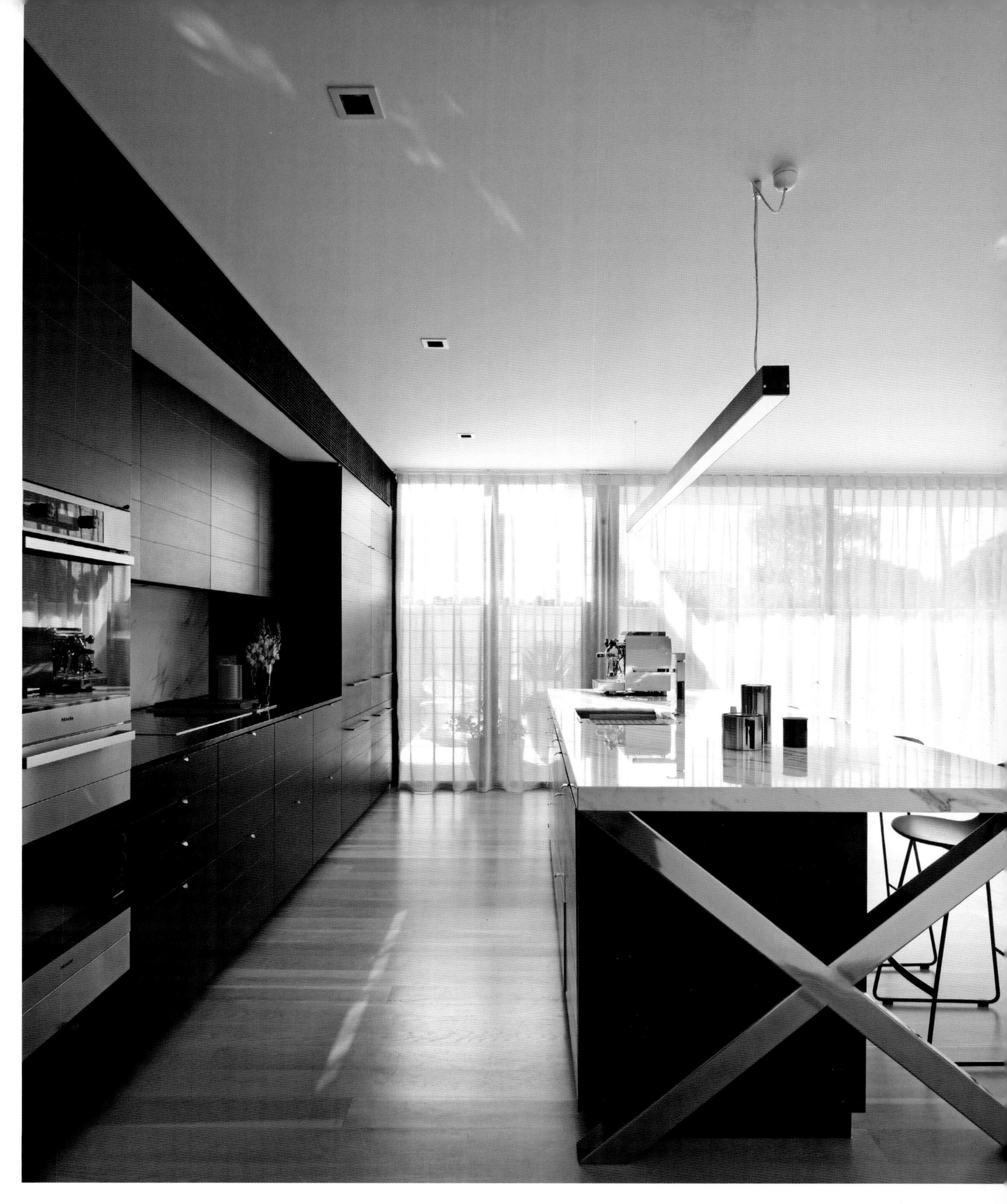

Opposite *Bringing a sophisticated gleam to the warm chocolate timber of this kitchen in the Melbourne house are the aged mirror panelling on the walls, the Rollo Cluster lights and the stunning custom-made shelving.*

Above *The kitchen of the house in Brighton is minimalist yet displays layering in its textures and finishes – the horizontal routed line on the black-stained oak cabinets, the crossed legs and marble top of the island bench, and the pendant light.*

CONTRAST

Contrast generates visual excitement and creative tension in a room, preventing a space from appearing flat or bland. It uses an interplay of finishes, fabrics, colours and pieces to keep your eyes moving around a space, thereby making a design more dynamic. There's a good reason why we pair a black suit with a white shirt. Opposites don't just attract – they look great together.

My first lesson in the importance of contrast came through studying the work of the legendary late English designer David Hicks, who outlined drapes and blinds with a different colour, a technique that was so simple yet made an incredible impact. Since the era of Hicks, many interior design greats have taken up the call. The late Austrian-born Australian architect Harry Seidler often used black window frames in his predominantly white buildings, as well as offsetting hard lines with carefully placed curves. More recently, contemporary heavyweights such as Kelly Wearstler and Jonathan Adler use a lot of black and white, and bold defined looks. For an example outside the world of interiors, you need look no further than the dramatic monochrome appeal of a timelessly chic Chanel store.

I've begun here by mentioning the use of monochromes by designers and, indeed, the classic combination of black and white is one of the simplest and most powerful illustrations of the effectiveness of contrast. But merely juxtaposing those tones isn't enough to make a dynamic composition – you also need to create links of theme, purpose, finish or texture, so the interplay between tones comes alive.

The powder room of the house in Sydney's Bellevue Hill features monochromes in a number of finishes that celebrate the principle of contrast. The sharp geometrics of the marble floor are juxtaposed with the organic swirls of wallpaper above, which soften the black and white to create a mid-tone mix. Between the two surfaces are blocks of grey marble and black tiles, linking them through palette but also providing a visual resting spot. Introducing a texture that stands out against the monochromes, the chrome lights and legs of the vanity bring a sophisticated sheen, with the white of its marble top highlighted by the simple flower display. The entire room is a picture of chic, considered, layered elegance, full of movement and interest.

Contrast is a dialogue, a lively conversation between different elements. Without it, no one's talking and the effect is hushed, dull. Too much of the same type of colour, a scarcity of textures, everything in a similar style, and the design's impact is dimmed. Without contrast there is no drama – and we all need a bit of drama in our lives.

WHERE TO WORK IT

Once you've reached the stage of layering your pieces, it's a highly rewarding challenge to play with contrast. Following are the main areas where I believe it can best be applied.

COLOUR AND PATTERN

Hues and prints allow you to play with contrast on a vast spectrum that can range from an element as large as a wall or floor finish to the smallest addition of a cushion or vase. It's no secret that I am a fan of black and white – the combination really works to highlight the other elements in a room. In the den of the contemporary Brisbane house, monochromes and patterns mix to create dramatic spaces. Against the strong, smooth black leather of an armchair, a curtain featuring small geometrics brings a soft, delicate balance.

In the library and study of the Sutton Forest country house black and white almost appear to take turns in the starring role, with predominantly black curtains revealing a crisp white trim, and white chairs and rugs outlined or decorated in black. The effect is seamless yet full of interest, with the interplay of pieces and palettes keeping your eye moving around the room. The house's master bedroom takes the juxtaposition further, showcasing the effectiveness of paint in bringing contrast to a room. Having already featured a fair amount of panelling in the house, I was hesitant to use more, yet I still wanted its effect. I decided to use paint in black, white and grey to simulate panelling and outlines, and the effect is strong and visually captivating. The walls work with the furniture of the room to build a clever and cohesive whole.

SHAPE

A move as simple as offsetting a rectangular sofa with a round coffee table can inject an instant dynamic of contrasting shapes. There's something about circles that seems to bring harmony and completion to a space. Organic, pure and visually calming, a circle can often present a neat stylistic break from

Previous page *A study in monochromes features on the landing of the Melbourne house, with the tones of the ornaments and painting highlighted by the intricate gold design of a Porta Romana Honeycomb console table.*

Opposite *In this powder room of the Bellevue Hill house the contrast between black and white in the bold marble floor is echoed in a softer form by the Fornasetti Malachite wallpaper.*

an abundance of angles. The contemporary Brisbane house – where we added two round coffee tables to a room dominated by angles – features plays on shape throughout. The contrast between lines and curves makes its most powerful statement in the ceiling of the den, where we installed a round coffer to offset a profusion of angles. Not only does it serve to anchor the pendant light, it also helps to soften a room that was looking a little too masculine. Here, too, the addition of a leather ottoman that mirrors the shape of the coffer balances the composition, even enhancing the effect of the contrasting chevron timber treatment on the doors behind.

SIZE

When you're arranging ornaments, the variety of sizes is one of the factors that give them their impact. A tall, cylindrical vase next to a small, round one allows each to shine, while a group of different candles creates its own story. But it's not just accessories where you can play with contrasting sizes – fabric and wallpaper patterns offer perfect opportunities to mix up the scale, while furniture and even cabinetry can benefit from a touch of drama. In the kitchen of the Edwardian house in Croydon, the rows of arch tiles are reflected in the exaggerated arch panels of the cabinets and cupboard doors. The result is cohesive yet impressive, a clever play on proportion.

FINISH

Hard and soft, rough and smooth, matt and gloss – an obvious place where contrast occurs almost naturally in houses is in the walls, floors, curtains, rugs and furniture. The interplay between textures is one of the most pleasing contrasts in the house, stimulating our sense of touch as well as our sense of sight. Clearly, a rug or sofa on a hard timber floor is an easy way to achieve this, but you should also make sure to include a contrast in the surfaces themselves.

Interior architecture can also offer opportunities for contrast. In the Brisbane house the diagonal lines of the dark oak cabinetry stand out beautifully against the silver vein running through the marble of the living room and kitchen floors.

Kitchens and bathrooms can sometimes feel a little sterile due to all those smooth walls and surfaces. I've found that a good way to combat this is through the use of travertine.

Opposite *Without veering from the monochromes of the den in the contemporary Brisbane house, a contrast of finishes has been achieved through the softly patterned curtains behind the strong leather of the Herman Miller Eames lounge chair and ottoman.*

Addressing a similar challenge in another area, I believe an expanse of timber in a library or living room can benefit from the juxtaposition of textural grey or striking monochrome rugs and furniture fabrics. The tones and textures work well to draw out the warm tones of the timber, while preventing it from appearing too heavy and dominating the space.

ERA

A piece of vintage furniture sitting in a contemporary layout can visually enliven notions of texture, finish and style, while adding a layer of history. Artwork is a simple way to mix modes and periods – most of us think nothing of featuring paintings of different genres in a room, and with good reason as they bring further interest to a space. Accessories can serve the same function and, indeed, most houses tend to feature a blend of old and new, of loved objects and eBay finds, family heirlooms and recently hoarded treasures.

STATEMENT

Intense bursts of colour, pattern and other standout features are easy ways to bring contrast and unexpected elements to a room. A single vibrant hue can set off a room's existing palette to perfection, coming into its own through a lamp base, cushion or throw. A statement piece of furniture will boldly claim its position in a room, offsetting the other pieces yet still conversing with them in a dynamic interplay. The almost otherworldly smooth lines of a white oval bath in the contemporary Brisbane house make it a feature piece against the geometric tiles, giving it luminosity and brilliance.

GENDER

We all joke about 'his' and 'hers' spaces, but masculine and feminine elements needn't always be separated. Many of my clients want different things from the one space and part of my challenge is to make both work together. In the Clontarf house we combined a desire for white panelled ceilings with a love of bright colour; in the Geelong country house we merged a rustic, industrial vision with a more dressed, glamorous one. I think anything is possible if you find a common link to unite the disparate elements. If they share something, whether it's palette, theme, finish or purpose, then the different styles, should create an exciting dialogue.

Picture some of those great old-school Hollywood film pairings – Cary Grant and Grace Kelly, Fred Astaire and Ginger Rogers, Humphrey Bogart and Lauren Bacall – and the frisson they brought to the screen. In the world of interiors, the result is no different: unlikely partnerships and lively combinations excite you with the creative tension they generate.

5 SIMPLE WAYS TO ADD CONTRAST

Playing with juxtaposition is fun and rewarding. Here are a few relatively easy yet effective ideas to try.

1 BRING MONOCHROME INTO THE MIX

Black and white is the ultimate striking contrast, and one you can introduce into the very foundations of your design, not just the accessories. Try outlining white walls in black paint or offsetting them with dark or black window frames for a dramatic effect. Or consider adding a black benchtop or island bench to an all-white kitchen.

2 CHOOSE ANY SHADE OF GREY

If monochrome is the black tie of interior design, then grey and white is its morning suit. Elegant and classic, it produces a softer effect than black and white while still offering a striking, formal pairing. White accessories and trims against grey walls result in a neat, tailored finish.

3 TAKE A CURTAIN CALL

A soft, floating shimmer of curtains or gentle unfolding of blinds brings a beautiful contrast to the hard surfaces of the surrounding walls and ceilings. It also adds texture, warmth and another layer of interest to a room.

4 PAY THE PIPER

Contrasting piping on cushions adds definition without being over the top. There's a reason contrasting colours are known as complementary colours – the hues that sit opposite each other on the colour wheel often work really well together. Similarly, a contrasting trim, braid or border will subtly highlight the effect of a curtain or blind.

5 SHOW YOUR COLOURS

Adding a touch of colour to a room is one of the easiest and most rewarding ways to make a statement. If you've built up your layers in neutrals, then it's great to choose a hue that will stand out against them while also lending vibrancy. Cushions, throws, furnishings, accessories and even flowers all offer a chance to introduce a dynamic tone.

In the master bedroom of the Sutton Forest country house I used black and white painted outlines to simulate panels and provide a strong counterpoint to the grey walls. The lines are echoed by the posts of the bed, with the rug tying the palette together.

Opposite *The kitchen of the Edwardian house in Croydon features a clever contrast of scale, with the arches of the Fornasetti tiles juxtaposed by the large arches in the cupboard panelling. Both are cohesive reminders of the arches in the house's vestibule.*

Above *In the house's family room the warm tones of a Jonathan Adler Bond coffee table and curves of a feature vase stand out against the monochrome geometrics of one of my rugs and the custom-made cabinets behind.*

Previous page *By installing a round coffer in the den of the contemporary Brisbane house and mirroring it with an ottoman below, I was able to introduce the curves required to offset the angles of the furniture and the chevron timber treatment on the doors.*

Opposite and above *Contrasts of tone, shape and texture are central to the library and study of the Sutton Forest country house, with elements such as the rug and cushion patterns, curtain trim and ottoman fringe providing detailed finishing touches.*

YVES SAINT LAURENT
FRANK LLOYD WRIGHT THE HOUSES

Previous page *The intricate lines of the carpet in my Darlinghurst apartment are echoed in the dining table legs, the dining chairs and the light. Organic-shaped accessories in different finishes juxtapose these.*

Opposite and above *In counterpoint to the repeated geometrics of the Brisbane bathroom, the smooth curves and solid white surface of an Apaiser bath make it a feature piece.*